Annual 2014

EGMONT

We bring stories to life

First published in Great Britain 2013
by Egmont UK Limited,
The Yellow Building, 1 Nicholas Road,
London W11 4AN

Writer: Polly Cheeseman
Designers: Kate Merritt, Maddy Wright
Editorial Assistant: Rachel Thompson
Group Editor: Kate Graham
Group Art Editor: Ant Gardner

© 2013 Disney Enterprises, Inc.

ISBN 978 1 4052 6646 8
54720/1
Printed in Italy

This fairy-tastic annual belongs to

....
Write your name here.

Disney Fairies

What's inside...

Disney FAIRIES

TinkerBell and the SECRET of the WINGS

A chance to win
£150 of book tokens!
See page 67 for details.

NATIONAL BOOK tokens

Your Fairy Friends

Follow the sparkly trail to say "hello" to all the magical fairies!

Rosetta

Pretty Rosetta is a garden fairy. She looks after all the flowers in Pixie Hollow.

Fawn

Friendly animal fairy Fawn is great fun to be around. She can talk to animals.

Tinker Bell

Tink is a tinker fairy. She loves mending broken things and coming up with new inventions!

Answer on page 65.

Silvermist

Water-talent fairy
Silvermist is able to
turn water into any
shape she likes.

Iridessa

Warm and sunny
Iridessa is a light-talent
fairy. She loves lighting
the fireflies at dusk.

Periwinkle

Frost fairy Periwinkle
enjoys ice-sliding on
frozen waterfalls!

9

Let's Meet Periwinkle

Find out more about the frost fairy from Winter Woods!

Fairy Talent

Periwinkle is a frost fairy. She loves frosting the leaves of Winter Woods, making amazing frost swirls and sledging down frozen waterfalls!

Icy Reading

Periwinkle is full of curiosity about how the warm fairies live. She reads ice books about the Pixie Dust Tree in Pixie Hollow – this supplies all fairies with their ration of pixie dust!

Secret Sister

When Periwinkle first meets Tinker Bell, their wings sparkle and glow. This is because they are actually sisters – they were born of the same laugh.

Wintery Wonderland

It is always cold in Winter Woods, where Peri lives. The land includes the Icicle Cave, the Frost Forest and the Hall of Winter – a grand library full of ancient books.

Snow Flurry

Two of these snowflakes are identical. Can you spot the matching pair?

a

b

c

d

e

f

Answer on page 65.

Peri's Puzzles

There's always so much to do in Winter Woods! Can you help Periwinkle solve these tricky teasers?

Shadow Fairies

Can you match each of the fairies below to their shadows?

1

2

3

4

a

b

c

d

Lost Treasure

Periwinkle has dropped one of her 'found things' in the snow. Help her find it by looking at the list and working out which object is missing.

Key
Locket
Thimble

Button
Cotton reel
Coin

Fairy Wish

Peri has a special wish to visit somewhere.
Can you work out where it is, using the key below?

Key

E	H	I	L
O	P	W	X

Colour

Brighten up these
frosty leaves by giving
them some colour!

Wintery World

Tink wants to visit Peri in Winter Woods. Can you help her find the right path through the maze?

Start

Count
How many snowflakes will Tink pass by on her way?

Finish

Answers on page 65.

Snowy Search

Can you find these wintery words hidden in the grid below? Tick them off as you go!

R	G	E	G	N	S	E	M	O
K	L	C	R	Y	S	T	A	L
N	I	Y	G	F	P	R	A	W
F	S	I	C	E	A	Q	I	I
R	T	U	J	N	R	N	A	N
O	E	C	E	E	K	P	U	T
S	N	O	W	F	L	A	K	E
T	U	L	S	Z	E	S	M	R
I	Y	D	P	S	K	A	T	E

Clue
The words read across and down.

- [ ] COLD
- [ ] WINTER
- [ ] SPARKLE
- [ ] CRYSTAL
- [ ] GLISTEN
- [ ] SNOWFLAKE
- [ ] FROST
- [ ] ICE
- [ ] SKATE

Answers on page 65.

Colour
Use your prettiest
pens to colour in this
picture of Peri
and Tink.

Adventure on Ice

Read the magical story below.
When you see a picture, shout
out the right word.

Tinker Bell

Periwinkle

Winter Woods

Frozen Waterfall

It was a hot day, and wanted to

cool off. "I know," she thought, "I'll

visit ." She set off straight

away and on reaching the river, she jumped along

the log bridge to . was delighted to see

 . "Let's go ice-skating!" she suggested.

 thought that sounded like fun. She

followed to a beautiful .

"This is my favourite place to skate,"

18

said. "I'm sure you'll love skating here, too."

But  suddenly felt a bit worried.

"I don't have any ice-skates," she said sadly.

"Here you go!" giggled  . She had made

a fairy-sized pair of skates out of two paperclips!

"Come on!" called  , gliding onto the  .

Carefully,  stepped out onto the ice.

"Whoa!" she squealed, as she skidded about.

"Don't worry," said  . "I'll teach you." She took

her sister's hand and whirled her gently around the

 . "You're great!"  laughed. "I'll soon

be an expert skater like you," chuckled

 . "It must run in the family!"

The End

Look and Find

Tink and Fawn are seeing the animals off on their trip to Winter Woods. Look at the scene and then answer the questions.

a How many bunnies can you see?

b Point to this detail in the scene.

c Are the stoats looking happy or sad?

....

d What do you think Fawn is telling Tink?

"Warm fairies like you and me are not allowed in the Winter Woods!" ☐

"Let's sneak across now. Who cares if the cold will destroy our wings!" ☐

e Who is wearing the green dress?
Trace her name below:

Tinker Bell

Write

Unjumble the letters to reveal something in the picture.

WNSO

Answers on page 65.

Let's Meet Tinker Bell

Join us to discover lots of fun facts about your favourite fairy!

Fairy Talent

Tinker Bell is a special tinker fairy. She has her own workshop, and repairs all sorts of pots and pans.

Exciting Inventions

Tink always tries to be useful and creative. Her favourite inventions are a clever acorn crusher and a colourful flower sprayer.

Magical Adventures

Tink loves to explore beyond Pixie Hollow. She flies to the Mainland to find lost things, but she has been known to get into trouble!

Tinker Bell was given her name because her voice sounds like a little tinkling bell.

Loyal Friend

Tink's fairy friends are very important to her. She promises never to let them down, and is always kind and fun to be around.

Pot Puzzle

Can you find the different pots below in Tink's workshop? Tick a circle as you spot each one.

Answers on page 65.

23

Once Upon a Time

It's evening time and Tinker Bell is visiting a house on the Mainland. Through the keyhole, she can see a little girl being read a bedtime story.

...and so the princess kissed the frog, who turned into a prince!

And they lived happily ever after.

Wow!

Tink can't wait to get home...
so she can find a frog to kiss!

Back in Pixie Hollow...

Frogs! Where are you?

What's she doing?

Finally Tink finds some frogs...

Hooray!

But Tink has startled them and they leap away.

Don't go!

Tink flies after the frogs and catches one.

Keep still! I'm going to turn you into a prince!

CROAK?!?

MMM, WAH!

But the kiss hasn't worked.

Hmmm?

What was supposed to happen?

Tink explains that the frog was supposed to turn into a prince.

That's what happened in the story on the Mainland.

26

Iridessa tells Tink that humans tell lots of stories on the Mainland...

...but not all of them are true. Some of them are fairy tales.

Oh! It sounded so real!

As the fairies fly off, Rosetta tells Tink not to worry about it anymore. But Tink still believes that, sometimes, fairy tales really can come true!

The End

Froggy Fun!

Can you help Tinker Bell complete these fun frog activities?

Pond Play

The frogs are hiding from Tink! Can you spot five in the picture below?

Kiss Trail!

Which trail should Tink take so she can kiss the frog?

a
b
c
d

Answers on page 65.

Count

How many water lilies are growing along the way?

29

Tinker Time

Tink loves to fix broken things. Can you help her by solving these tricky fairy puzzles?

Matching Fun

Lizzy's got lots of things for Tink to mend. Can you match each object to the tool that will repair it?

1
2
3
4

a
b
c
d

Pattern Perfect

Tink is making pretty patterns for her new p
Use the right colour to finish these sequence

a

b

Colour
Add some lovely colours to this happy picture of Tink and Blaze.

Let's Meet Rosetta

Time to find out a little more about this talented garden fairy!

Fairy Talent

Rosetta cares for all the plants and flowers in Pixie Hollow. She paints the flowers pretty colours, helps them open their petals and sprays them with sweet scented perfumes.

Scented Home

Rosetta has made her home in a rose-blossom chalet in Buttercup Canyon.

Pretty Petals

Rosetta always likes to look her best and she dresses in the silkiest pink and red rose petals.

Beautiful Blooms

Rosetta has been watering these pretty flowers. Can you work out which one has grown the biggest?

Beauty Tips

Rosetta loves fashion and beauty. She shares her tips on looking fairy-fabulous with all her friends!

Favourite Flower

Can you find four letters hidden on these pages and rearrange them to spell the name of Rosetta's favourite flower?

_____ _____ _____ _____

Pixie Puzzles

There's always lots to do in Pixie Hollow. Can you help the fairies with these puzzles?

Flower Fun

Rosetta wants some beautiful flowers. Follow the clues below to work out which basket she will choose.

Clues

1 The basket isn't brown.

2 It contains purple flowers.

3 It has two yellow flowers.

Rosetta will choose basket...

a

b

c

d

Pretty Pairs

Tink has spotted lots of colourful butterflies. Draw lines to match them into pairs.

a

b

c

h

f

d

g

e

Prickly Friend

Join up all the dots to find out who has come out to play with Fawn!

31
29
27
25
21
19
33
23
17
30 28 26 24 22 20
34 32
18
15
16
13
14
12
1
4
2
8
11
3
7
5 6
9 10

Answers on page 66.

35

Question of Colour

At the Fairy Camp, Fawn is in need of a favour. She spots Rosetta and wonders if she will help.

PAT PAT

Fawn asks Rosetta if she will look after her butterfly friend while she flies off to get something.

Sure thing, Buttercup!

Thanks! I'll be back in a wingbeat!

As Rosetta is waiting, she suddenly has an idea. If she can paint flowers, then maybe she can paint butterflies, too!

She fetches her paintbrush and paints and slowly gets to work on the butterfly.

It'll be a surprise for Fawn!

SWISH SPLASH

But the butterfly flies into the air, spraying paint everywhere!

Hey! That was so rude!

Rosetta can't understand what is wrong.

Rosetta wonders if the butterfly is upset because it doesn't like the colours she is using.

So, she sets about mixing some of her paints together to find the perfect shade.

Eventually, Rosetta makes a pretty lilac colour and a soft pink colour.

You must like these!

Rosetta starts painting the butterfly again.

SPLISH SPLASH

But it flies into the air once more, and Rosetta is left covered in paint.

When Fawn arrives back, she can't believe her eyes. She asks Rosetta if she has tried to paint the butterfly, and Rosetta nods unhappily.

I wanted to do you a favour!

Fawn explains that the butterfly has ticklish wings! She then shows Rosetta what she has been to get.

It's a flower-sprayer! Fawn wanted one so she could paint the butterfly without it flying away. The fairies laugh, then Rosetta looks down at her dress – at least she has made two colours that look good on her!

The End

Spot the Difference

There are five differences in the bottom picture.
Colour a flower as you spot each one!

Answers on page 66.

Colour

Rosetta can't decide what colour outfit to wear today. Help her by using your favourite colour to complete the picture.

41

Let's Meet Fawn

Fawn is a friendly animal fairy. Let's find out more about her and her animal friends.

Fairy Talent

Fawn is an animal-talent fairy. She can speak to all kinds of creatures and is always ready to help an animal in trouble.

Playful Pixie

Fun-loving Fawn loves playing games! She is a real joker and often plays giggly tricks on the other fairies.

Count

Count how many pine cones like this one are hidden on these pages.

Nuts about Animals

Fawn loves collecting tasty nuts and acorns for her cute squirrel friends to eat.

Nature Lover

Like her fairy friends, Fawn loves nature. She lives in a tree house made from a giant pine cone, in Pine Forest. Fawn's favourite possession is also a pine cone!

Odd One Out

These cheeky squirrels look the same, but one is different! Can you work out which one?

a

b

c

Answers on page 66.

The Missing Butterfly

The fairies are excited. Later there will be a big party celebrating the changing of the seasons. Fawn is getting ready to rehearse the twenty-one butterfly salute...

Right! On three, you all fly into the air together!

But when Fawn counts the butterflies she discovers one is missing!

Twenty butterflies aren't enough for the twenty-one butterfly salute!

42

Oh dear, where is the other butterfly?

Fawn looks for the missing butterfly, while the other fairies keep working.

Fawn thinks maybe the missing butterfly is in one of the lanterns.

Fawn checks each lantern for the missing butterfly, but the lanterns are empty.

What a mess!

Who's going to help me hang the lanterns back up?

Uh-oh! I will, of course!

45

After she's helped Iridessa, Fawn thinks she can see the missing butterfly in Rosetta's basket.

Gotcha, you little rascal!

SWISH

But she's wrong again. It's only a petal!

Eek! My flower decorations!

After she's tidied up, Fawn goes back to her butterflies.

What can I do?

Fawn can't believe it! The missing butterfly is playing with the bubbles the tadpoles have made!

46

As the tadpoles are busy making the bubbles, the butterfly is having fun popping them!

PFFF!

Oh!

POP

She's spent the whole afternoon playing with the bubbles!

The missing butterfly mystery is solved!

POP

You could've let me know, silly!

If I'd have known you were here, maybe I wouldn't have caused so much trouble! Hee! Hee!

Fawn's happy. Now that she's found the twenty-first butterfly, her salute is bound to be perfect!

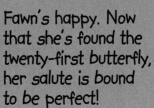

The End

Fairy Fun

Join your fairy friends for lots of fun by completing these activities.

Fairy Close-Ups

Can you work out which fairy is shown in each of these close-ups?

a

b

c

d

48

Find and Count

Count how many of each of these items there are in the scene.

 a ☐

 b ☐

 c ☐

 d ☐

Who am I?

Read these clues, then see if you can work out who the mystery fairy is.

I have brown hair.

❀❀❀

My name begins with an 'F.'

❀❀❀

I can talk to animals.

Answers on page 66.

Let's Meet Iridessa

Learn lots of bright facts about Iridessa's favourite hobbies and fairy talents.

Fairy Talent

Iridessa can create and shape light. During the day, she makes sunbeams to help plants grow, and at night she lights up the fireflies.

Fabulous Fashion

Iridessa makes all her dresses from pretty yellow flowers. Her favourite dresses are those made from sunflowers and buttercups.

Rainbow Fun

Iridessa loves making colourful rainbows with the water fairies. She tries to make them big and bright so that everyone can see them!

Colour

Add some pretty colours to the butterflies on these pages.

Sunny Smile

Iridessa is a warm, happy fairy. Like a ray of sunlight, when she's around, everybody is in a cheerful mood.

Odd One Out

Can you spot which firefly is different to the others?

a

b

c

d

e

Answer on page 66.

A Starless Night

A full moon is shining brightly in Pixie Hollow. Tink is watching Iridessa dive off the clouds.

Watch this, Tink!

Wow! How wonderful!

Iridessa flies back up. She asks Tink if she looked like a shooting star.

Now Iridessa's mentioned shooting stars, Tink wonders why they haven't seen any tonight.

In fact, the fairies can only *see* one star in the whole sky...the star that leads to Never Land.

Hmmm...

Iridessa tells Tink about an old legend that says when the stars don't shine, someone in Never Land is in trouble.

Gasp!

The fairies fly off in search of anyone in trouble. They soon spot a baby owl splashing about in the river. He can't get out of the water on his own.

Look, Iridessa!

Hooo!

Tink and Iridessa try to pull the baby owl out of the water but he's too heavy.

Argh!

The fairies wonder what to do. Suddenly Tink has an idea...

We can use this tall grass as a rope!

Tink weaves lots of blades of grass together to make a strong rope.

Ready? Go!

The fairies soon pull the baby owl to safety.

Hooray!

Hooray!

Tink tells the baby owl they'll take him home.

Soon the baby owl is back in his nest with his mother.

Hoo, hoo!

Now that the baby owl is safe, the stars come out again. With such a beautiful, twinkling background, Iridessa's glimmering trail looks even more spectacular than before!

Wonderful!

The End

Flower Power

The fairies love beautiful blooms. Can you help them answer these tricky teasers?

Fairy Code

Iridessa has picked a pretty blue flower. Can you work out what it is, using the code below?

U E B L

_ _ _ _ _ _

Find the Flowers

Reading across and down, can you find these flowers hidden in the wordsearch? Colour a flower as you spot each one.

- LILY
- ROSE
- DAFFODIL
- DAISY
- TULIP
- PANSY

H	O	P	L	A	C	K	P	O
I	D	A	I	S	Y	U	L	U
R	E	N	L	W	A	N	G	R
I	R	S	Y	E	S	S	T	O
D	X	Y	P	H	L	E	I	S
E	F	O	L	B	D	E	N	E
D	A	F	F	O	D	I	L	T
J	L	R	V	E	K	T	S	M
A	T	U	L	I	P	C	E	A

Colour
Give Iridessa some magical colours as she rests on a sunflower.

Answers on page 66.

Let's Meet Silvermist

Find out about this calm and caring water fairy.

Fairy Talent

As a water talent fairy, Silvermist's job is to carry precious water droplets to plants and animals. She also creates mists in the air and ripples on streams.

Peace and Calm

With her relaxed attitude to life, Silvermist has the ability to smooth over squabbles between friends. She always sees the best in people.

Special Jobs

Creatures love the little ways that Silvermist helps them. She adds dew drops to spider webs and trains tadpoles to blow bubbles!

Water Sports

Silvermist loves spending time in and around water. One of her favourite activities is waterskiing on a teaspoon pulled by a hummingbird!

Magical Message

Silvermist enjoys sending secret messages! Use a mirror to reveal this one.

I LOVE WATERFALLS

Colour

Add a splash of colour to Silvermist.

Answer on page 66.

Water Games

It's a hot, hot day in Pixie Hollow. Tinker Bell decides to go down to the pond to cool down and visit Silvermist.

Hi, Silvermist! What are you doing?

Silvermist and her hummingbird friend are having fun water-skiing on a big spoon. Tink wants to have a go, too.

That looks like fun!

Silvermist hops off the spoon so that Tink can get on.

She explains that the key to water-skiing is balance, but it's harder than Tink expected!

As Tink struggles to stay afloat, the fairies haven't noticed Vidia watching them.

You're too clumsy, Tink!

Finally, Tink gets her balance and the hummingbird begins to pull the spoon.

Woahhhhh!

As the hummingbird gets faster and faster, the spoon starts spraying water everywhere! Vidia gets soaked!

Where are the brakes?!

SPLASH!

When Tink is safely back on land, she tells Silvermist she can't wait to have another go! Just then, Vidia appears and she's very angry.

Tink hadn't seen Vidia sitting on the leaf, and is very sorry for getting her wet.

Just look at what you've done!

Silvermist explains that it was only an accident, and she tells Vidia to look on the bright side...

...all of the fairies were trying to get cool, but only she actually did!

The End

A Fairy Friend

Which fairy would be your best friend?
Answer the questions below to find out!

1

If you were feeling sad,
would your best friend...

a Give you a present

b Give you a big hug

c Try to make you laugh

2

What do you do with
your best friend at weekends?

a Read an adventure story

b Go swimming

c Go for a walk in
   the park

3

If your best friend
gave you a pet, what
would it be?

a A lively, curious mouse

b A sweet, cuddly kitten

c A cute, fluffy duckling

Read the
panels below to
discover which fairy
would be your
best friend.

Mostly As

Tink would be your best
friend. She's full of fun
and would always have a
surprise in store for you!

Mostly Bs

Your best friend would be
Silvermist. She's kind and
caring and would know how to
cheer you up when you're sad!

Mostly Cs

Fawn would be your best
fairy friend. She's happy
and playful – you'd always
be smiling with her around!

Answers

Page 9 — Your Fairy Friends

Quick Quiz:
b - Rosetta.

Page 11 — Let's Meet Periwinkle

Snow Flurry:
Snowflakes b and f.

Pages 12-13 — Peri's Puzzles

Shadow Fairies:
1 - b, 2 - a, 3 - d, 4 - c.
Lost Treasure:
Coin.
Fairy Wish:
PIXIE HOLLOW.

Pages 14-15 — Wintery World

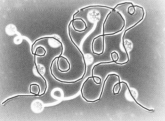

Count:
5 snowflakes.

Page 16 — Snowy Search

R	C	E	G	N	S	E	M	O
K	L	C	R	Y	S	T	A	L
N	I	Y	G	F	P	R	A	W
F	S	I	G	E	A	Q	I	I
R	T	U	J	N	R	N	A	N
D	E	C	E	E	K	P	U	T
P	I	N	D	W	F	A	K	E
T	U	L	S	Z	E	S	M	R
I	Y	D	P	G	K	A	T	E

Pages 20-21 — Look and Find

a) 4 bunnies.
c) Happy.
d) "Warm fairies like you and me are not allowed in the Winter Woods!"
e) Tinker Bell.
Write: SNOW.

Page 23 — Let's Meet Tinker Bell

Pot Puzzle:

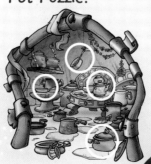

Pages 28-29 — Froggy Fun!

Pond Play:

Kiss Trail!: b
Count:
3 water lilies.

Page 30 — Tinker Time

Matching Fun:
1 - c, 2 - d, 3 - b, 4 - a.
Pattern Perfect:
a. Orange.
b. Pink.

Answers

Page 33 Let's Meet Rosetta

Beautiful Blooms:
d has grown biggest.
Favourite Flower:
rose.

Pages 34-35 Pixie Puzzles

Flower Fun:
Basket c.
Pretty Pairs:
a and g, b and e,
c and f, d and h.
Prickly Friend:
A hedgehog.

Page 40 Spot the Difference

Blaze has disappeared
from Tink's hand,
a petal on Rosetta's
skirt has changed
colour, Tink's pom-pom
is missing from her
right slipper, a second
butterfly has
appeared, a daffodil
has changed colour.

Page 43 Let's Meet Fawn

Count: 5 pine cones.
Odd One Out:
Squirrel a.

Pages 48-49 Fairy Fun

Fairy Close-Ups:
a - Silvermist, b - Rosetta,
c - Tinker Bell, d - Iridessa.
Find and Count:
4 fireflies, 2 water lilies,
1 ladybird, 2 frogs.
Who am I?:
Fawn.

Page 51 Let's Meet Iridessa

Odd one out: Firefly d.

Page 56 Flower Power

Fairy Code: BLUEBELL.
Find the Flowers:

H	O	P	L	A	C	K	P	Q
I	D	A	I	S	Y	U	L	U
R	E	N	L	W	A	N	G	R
I	R	S	Y	E	S	S	T	O
D	X	Y	P	H	L	E	I	S
E	F	O	L	B	D	E	N	E
D	A	F	F	O	D	I	L	T
J	L	R	V	E	K	T	S	M
A	T	U	L	I	P	C	E	A

Page 59 Let's Meet Silvermist

Magical Message:
I LOVE
WATERFALLS

66

Reader Survey

We'd love to know what you think about your Fairies Annual.

Ask a grown-up to help you fill in this form and post it to the address at the end by 28th February 2014, or you can fill in the survey online at:

www.egmont.co.uk/disneyfairies-survey2014

One lucky reader will win £150 of book tokens!
Five runners-up will win a £25 book token each.

NATIONAL BOOK tokens

---

1. Who bought this annual?

☐ Me
☐ Parent/guardian
☐ Grandparent
☐ Other (please specify)

....

2. Why did they buy it?

☐ Christmas present
☐ Birthday present
☐ I'm a collector
☐ Other (please specify)

....

---

3. What are your favourite parts of the Fairies Annual?

Stories	☐	Really like	☐	Like	☐	Don't like
Puzzles and quizzes	☐	Really like	☐	Like	☐	Don't like
Colouring	☐	Really like	☐	Like	☐	Don't like
Character profiles	☐	Really like	☐	Like	☐	Don't like
Facts	☐	Really like	☐	Like	☐	Don't like

---

4. Do you think the stories are too long, too short or about right?

☐ Too long
☐ Too short
☐ About right

5. Do you think the activities are too hard, too easy or about right?

☐ Too hard
☐ Too easy
☐ About right

6. Apart from Tinker Bell, who are your favourite characters in the Fairies Annual?

1. ....

2. ....

3. ....

7. Which other annuals have you bought this year?

1. ....

2. ....

3. ....

8. What is your favourite...

1. ...app? ....

2. ...website? ....

3. ...console game? ....

4. ...magazine? ....

5. ...book? ....

9. What are your favourite TV programmes?

1. ....

2. ....

3. ....

11. Would you like to get another Disney Annual again next year?

☐ Yes   ☐ No

Why? ....

....

....

10. Have you bought a Disney Annual before? If so, which ones?

1. ....

2. ....

3. ....

☐ Please send me the Egmont Monthly Catch-Up Newsletter

Thank you!
(Please ask your parent/guardian to complete)

Child's name: _____ Age: _____ Boy/Girl

Parent/guardian name: _____

Parent/guardian signature: _____

Parent/guardian email address: _____

Daytime telephone number: _____

Please cut out this form and post to:
Fairies Annual Reader Survey, Egmont UK Limited,
The Yellow Building, 1 Nicholas Road, London W11 4AN.

Don't miss Tinker Bell magazine!

Disney FAIRIES

FREE Fairy phone!

Disney FAIRIES

TinkerBell

www.disneyfairies.co.uk

Featuring all your favourite fairies

Fairy-tastic stories

Heaps of puzzles and fun

Pretty posters

Lovely colouring

All of this inside...

Stories
Colouring
Puzzles

FREE GIFT with every issue!

Available at all good newsagents and supermarkets.

On sale every month!